I AM A JEDI

EGMONT

We bring stories to life

This edition first published in Great Britain 2017
by Egmont UK Limited, The Yellow Building,
1 Nicholas Road, London W11 4AN.

© & TM 2017 Lucasfilm Ltd.

ISBN 978 0 6035 7422 1
68486/1
Printed in Estonia

To find more great *Star Wars* books, visit www.egmont.co.uk/starwars

Stay safe online. Any website addresses listed in this book are correct at the
time of going to print. However, Egmont is not responsible for content hosted by
third parties. Please be aware that online content can be subject to change and
websites can contain content that is unsuitable for children. We advise that all
children are supervised when using the internet.

STAR WARS

I AM A JEDI

By Christopher Nicholas

Illustrated by Ron Cohee

THIS BOOK BELONGS TO

I am a **JEDI**

I am a guardian who fights for peace and justice.

A Jedi's power comes from the **Force**, an energy field created by all living things that binds the galaxy together.

A Jedi can use the Force to

levitate objects . . .

leap **FAR**...

run **FAST**...

jump **HIGH**...

trick the weak-minded . . .

and **influence** others!

A Jedi wears
a hooded **cloak**.

Some
Jedi are
big.

Some Jedi are **small**.
Size matters not.

A Jedi's weapon is
the **lightsaber**.

It is a powerful **laser** sword
that can cut through anything.

A young Jedi in training
is called a **Padawan**.

Before becoming a Jedi Knight,
a Padawan must be taught by a Jedi
Master in the ways of the **Force**.

A Jedi should always be at **peace**.
Fighting is the last resort.

Hate and fear can lead a Jedi down the path to
the **dark side** of the Force.

**Anakin
Skywalker**

was once a
powerful Jedi
who gave in to
the dark side.

He became
Darth Vader—

Lord

of

the Sith.

The Sith are **the enemy** of
the Jedi. They are evil warriors
who use the Force to spread fear.

There can be only two Sith Lords at a time—a
master and an apprentice. The Jedi are in a constant
battle with the Sith to restore balance to the Force.

At the end of their
lives, all Jedi become
one with the Force.

Some continue to communicate
with the living as **Force Spirits**!

Would **YOU** like to be a Jedi?

THE END